PUZZLES, PATTERNS, AND PASTIMES

PUZZLES, PATTERNS, and PASTIMES

FROM THE WORLD OF MATHEMATICS

---

by Charles F. Linn

ILLUSTRATED BY LOU MYERS

DOUBLEDAY & COMPANY, INC., GARDEN CITY, NEW YORK

For
Jeff and Jenny,
Holly and Heather,
and Susan

An Introduction Which you don't really need to read. But the organization of this collection may cause a question or two. The "section" titles are not very enlightening—and deliberately so. The puzzles are pretty well scrambled.

My first thought was to make no grouping, by chapter or "section," but after being convinced that some such was desirable, I decided not to group by type—arithmetic, geometric, cards, coins, or shaggy dog—or by degree of difficulty. A person who prefers a particular type would probably feel disappointed to find that he has run through all of "his" type in one chapter and has nothing to look forward to.

And, I think it encouraging to come across an easy puzzle after working hard on some difficult ones, much as I enjoy the wrestling with difficult types.

All of which left me with no basis upon which to group except by "puzzles," "more puzzles," and the like.

Particular emphasis is placed on the "build your own" possibilities. I hope you will do just that. This is the real fun. And, in between building your own, have fun with these.

C. F. LINN
Turkey Hill, Connecticut
1969

Contents

PUZZLES, PATTERNS, AND PASTIMES

Puzzles are where you find them

1. In the back yard Looking out in the back yard one day, I saw an assortment of boys and dogs. Counting heads, I got twenty-two. Counting legs, I got sixty-eight. How many boys were in the yard?

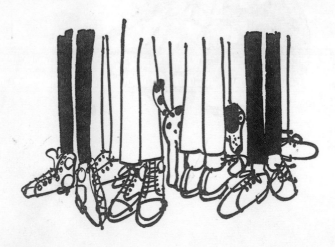

2. On the road to Syracuse As we were driving along the New York Thruway toward Syracuse, Jeff noticed that one sign said:

New York 320 miles
Syracuse 32 miles

"How about that," he said. "Just ten times as far from New York as from Syracuse."

"Well," I replied, "the sign told you that. But can you tell me how far we were from Syracuse when we were nine times as far from New York as from Syracuse?"

With a bit of mental number-juggling, Jeff came up with the right answer. Can you?

3. In a fifth-grade classroom A year or so ago I was playing that patterns game with a group of fifth-grade students. One of us would make up a rule and the other would try to guess it by giving him numbers and seeing what he would respond, according to his "rule."

Mike, who had not said much, who was, in fact, supposed to do poorly at arithmetic, finally spoke up and said that he had a pattern. Someone said to him, "One," and he responded, "Three." Another person said, "Two," and again he said, "Three." Immediately up went the hands of those students who thought they had guessed the pattern, but they went back down again when Mike replied, "Five" to an input of "Three."

What was the pattern he had in mind?

In case you need more evidence, here is a table of some pairs of numbers . . . "inputs" and Mike's responses:

inputs	1	2	3	4	5	6	7	8
Mike's responses	3	3	5	4	4	3	5	5

Just for the record, Mike's response to "1478" would have been "Thirty-four."

4. In the year of this book This book bears a 1969 copyright. Let's see what can be done with those digits 1, 9, 6, and 9. Use these four digits, *in that order,* with the signs for addition, subtraction, multiplication, division, and square root, to build the successive whole numbers. For example:

$$1 + \sqrt{9} + 6 - 9 = 1$$
$$1 + \sqrt{9} - 6 + \sqrt{9} = 1$$
or
$$(1 \cdot \sqrt{9} \cdot 6) \div 9 = 2$$

5. The hike Frankie and Bobby were off on a long hike. "We've walked an hour already, and we're only a fifth of the way there," complained Bobby. "Well," said Frankie, who had organized the expedition, "if we just walk one mile per hour faster, we'll cut a full hour off our time."

How far were the boys planning to walk?

6. In the button can Holly was sorting out buttons from the big button can. "How many do you have of each color?" asked her mother.

"Well," replied Holly, who never gave a straight answer when she could think of a complicated one, "there are sixty-six buttons altogether—twice as many whites as greens, one less blue than green, and seven more reds than greens."

How many buttons did she have of each color?

7. Who's got the button? When Jeff heard Holly's puzzle-answer to the rather simple question, he had to go her one better. Quickly he sorted out some buttons from the button can and announced, "There are twenty reds, twenty-four small buttons, and fifteen fancy buttons. Of these, eight are small red buttons but not fancy, six are large red fancy buttons, five are small and fancy but not red, and three are small, fancy red ones."

How many buttons had he in all?

8. From test scores "How did you make out on the test, Brian?" his father asked.

"Well, I got two more right than Sam did," replied Brian evasively.

"That doesn't tell me much," said his father. "How did you do percentwise?"

"I got 5 percent more than Sam did," murmured Brian.

How many questions were there on the test?

Puzzles are where you find them

9. In the change purse "Sounds like quite a pile of change," called David to his father, who had just dumped some coins on the table.

"Tell you what," observed his father after a minute. "If you can say how many coins of each kind I have, I'll give you

half the dimes. There are twice as many nickels as quarters, and seven fewer quarters than dimes. Altogether I have $2.95."

David figured out the number of each kind of coin. How much did he win?

10. When the principal calls The principal asked Mrs. Benjamin how many students she had in her nongraded math class. "Well," she replied, "three-fourths of them are less than twelve years old, two-thirds are less than eleven, and twelve are not yet ten years old. There are twice as many between ten and eleven as there are between eleven and twelve."

The principal murmured his thanks and went off to figure out how many students there were altogether. Can you help him?

11. A candle race Suppose you had two candles of exactly the same length, but one is of better quality so that it burns for five hours. The other burns only four hours. You light both candles at once. How soon will one be four times the length of the other?

12. Candy is for eating Holly and Heather were comparing the candy each had found in Mrs. Rarey's candy hunt. "If you give me one of your pieces," said Heather, "we'd both have the same number . . . and that'd be fair, 'cause you beat me to one piece I saw first."

"Yes," replied Holly, "but since I'm older, I should have more candy. Now, if you gave me one piece, I would have just twice as many as you have."

Needless to say, Heather did not agree to this idea. But how many pieces of candy does each girl have?

13. The copper coins Looking at their faces, you can tell quarters from pennies. So arrange four of each in such a way that you have two rows with just two quarters in each row, four rows with just two pennies in each row, and four rows with two quarters and one penny in each.

14. From any number The sum of the digits of a two-digit number is 5. If you write down this number, reverse the digits, write down this number, then subtract the smaller number from the larger, the difference is 27. What are the two numbers?

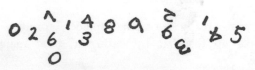

15. An octonary variation Here's a variation on that last problem: Suppose you were working in base 8. The sum of the digits of a two-digit number is 7. If you reverse the digits and subtract the smaller from the larger, the difference is 25. What was the original number?

16. The Christmas candy Jenny had received a large bag of candy for Christmas, and she was rapidly eating same. Her mother insisted that she cut down on the number of pieces she was eating.

"But they are really very small pieces," protested Jenny.

"You make up for that by eating a great many," replied her mother.

"Oh, all right," grumbled Jenny, "but I must cut down gradually, like Daddy always does on cigarettes. I'll eat three fewer pieces each day."

"I'll keep score," announced her mother.

During the next five days Jenny ate a total of seventy pieces of candy. How many did she eat each day?

17. On the checkerboard How many squares are there on a checkerboard? Careful now, before you say, "sixty-four," because that obviously isn't right.

18. By plane and train In going from Turkey Hill to West Overshoe I actually traveled for seven hours and thirty minutes. I went part way by bus and part by plane, which averaged five times the average of the bus. If the total distance is 1050 miles, what speeds did the bus and plane average?

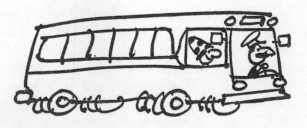

19. Zeros for guesses To discourage guessing on a math test, Frankie's teacher announced that he would take off seven points for every wrong answer.

"That's not fair," yelped Frankie. "You only give five points for a correct answer."

"Just answer those you are sure of, then," replied the teacher.

But Frankie was always sure of himself and had visions of a bonus for getting all twenty-four problems correct. He answered them all and "broke even"—an even zero, that is. How many problems did he answer correctly?

20. Hit the nail on the head Jeff was helping Mr. Billings with some carpentry work. He noticed that over the long run Mr. Billings drove five nails to his three (possibly because Jeff was counting when he should have been hammering). Mr. Billings was called to the telephone, and Jeff drove thirty nails during the ten minutes he was gone. If they started hammering at nine o'clock, at what time did they finish driving 350 nails?

21. On the clock Half an hour ago it was twice as long after noon as it is from now until midnight. What time is it now?

22. And easy An hour ago 'twas as long after noon as 'twill be in another hour till midnight. The time now?

Puzzles

1. Guess a sum Have a friend write a five-digit number on a piece of paper. Suppose he writes, "58715."

Now, you write on another piece of paper "258713," but fold this paper and don't let him see it. Possibly a neutral party will hold the paper.

Now, have the person who wrote the first number write another five-digit number right below it, say:

```
                    58715
                    64892
and you write       35107
then if he writes   72514
you write           27485
```

and let him add to get 258713
Just as you predicted. What's the secret?

2. Change by eleven Making change for a dollar with ten coins is easy. Can you change a dollar into eleven coins? How about a lucky thirteen coins for a dollar?

3. An agricultural problem Three farmers raise 165 acres of grain. Jones owns 100 acres of the land and Smith owns sixty-five acres. Jingleheimer pays the others $110 rent. How should Jones and Smith divide this money if the grain is shared equally?

4. Up and down the mountain A
man drove up a mountain,
averaging fifteen miles per hour.
What speed must he average on
the return trip in order to average
thirty miles per hour for the round
trip?

5. The inverted plate Mr. Aylesworth sent Tommy out to
fasten the new license plate on the car. Tommy got the plate
on securely but managed to turn the plate upside down. When
his father pointed out this small error, Tommy merely shrugged.

"It's an easy mistake to make, Pop," he observed, "since the
number reads okay upside down. Anyway, your license plate
now reads 78,975 more than it would have right side up. High
score wins, you know."

"Swell," said his father facetiously. "I'll mention that to the
trooper when he stops me."

What was the number on the license plate, anyway?

6. Don't send a boy If four men and six boys do a job in
the same time that six men and three boys take to do the
job, how many boys do the work of one man?

7. No change with multiplication Can you find a fraction such that when the digits of the numerator are multiplied and placed over the digits of the denominator, multiplied, the new fraction has the same value as the original?

8. The missing digits Fill in the blanks to make this a correct multiplication example.

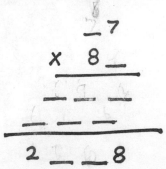

9. A circle of circles Put numbers in for the letters in the following diagram so that you have all the numbers from 1 through 14, and each circle totals 21.

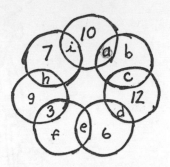

10. To build a skinny rectangle Can you cut a 3″-by-8″ rectangle into two pieces and reassemble them to form a 2″-by-12″ rectangle?

11. Better late than never A train scheduled for a long non-stop overland haul broke down after traveling an hour. After another hour such repairs were made that the train could proceed but only at half its usual rate, and it arrived at its destination three hours late. If it could have averaged ten miles an hour faster after the breakdown, it would have cut one hour off the time. What is the distance between stations?

12. Don't drop a stitch If a ball of yarn six inches in diameter will make one pair of gloves, how many identical pairs of gloves will a ball twelve inches in diameter make?

13. The operation makes no difference Can you split 100 into four parts so that when you add 4 to one part you get the same answer as when you multiply 4 by another part, or subtract 4 from another part, or divide the last part by 4?

14. Money by the barrel Which would you rather have, a barrel full of silver dollars or a barrel full of silver dimes? (I suppose I need not say "silver," but somehow the idea of a barrel full of copper dimes doesn't appeal at all.)

15. An even hundred Can you insert addition and subtraction signs among the following digits to get an expression equal to 100?

1 2 3 4 5 6 7 8 9

16. Father and son

My father's age I just found out.
He's four times as old as me,
But after only five more years
His age'll be mine times three.

You can sure guess what I'll ask of you,
So speak without delay.
My father's age—and also mine—
Quick now, what do you say?

17. Puzzle-posing patron "I'm going for my coffee break," said the one postal clerk to another. "Here comes that nut who always makes a puzzle out of his order."

The second clerk couldn't hide, so he braced himself for the encounter. "Morning," said this favored customer, beaming. "I want a dollar's worth of eight-cent and five-cent stamps . . . three times as many five-cent stamps as eight-cent, please."

Then, before the clerk had a chance to collect his wits, the customer pointed out, "You can't do that and have it come out an even dollar. So throw in another eight-cent, and that'll use the dollar."

The clerk was rather used to him by then, so he quickly figured out the correct number of stamps. Can you?

18. Prices are up "I'm ready for that guy this time," muttered the postal clerk about the customer who always posed puzzles. "The rates have changed."

Up to the window bounced the ebullient patron. "This is an easy one," he announced. "I need the same number of four-cent postcards as five-cent stamps . . . and that'll leave a penny change out of a dollar."

"Sorry, sir," replied the clerk, "but postcards are now five cents and first-class mail is six cents. Rates just went up today.

But if you add another penny, you can get just as many stamps for first-class mail and almost as many postcards."

"Forgot all about the price increase," said the customer, "but I'll go along with your suggestion."

How many stamps and postcards did he get?

19. A triangle of coins   Arrange ten coins like this:

Now, move only three coins to produce this arrangement:

20. Rows of three or four   Can you rearrange this array of nine coins so that they form rows of four coins to the row?

(No fair tossing out one coin!)

21. Jumping coins Place ten coins—or any suitable counter-(feit?)—in a row, like this:

(I have numbered the positions for convenience.)

Your move, in this game, is to jump a coin over the two coins next to it, and place it atop the third coin. For example, coin 1 can be moved to the top of coin 4, coin 5 to coin 8, and so on. Moving the coins in this way, can you arrange the ten coins in five evenly spaced piles of two coins each?

(Once you place a coin on top of another, you can't take it off.)

22. The chicken came first If three
hens lay three eggs in three days,
how many eggs will three hundred
hens lay in three hundred days?

23. The eggs came first On the
other hand, if three hens lay three
eggs in three days, how many hens
will be needed to produce three
hundred eggs in three hundred
days?

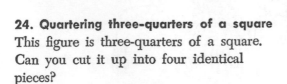

24. Quartering three-quarters of a square
This figure is three-quarters of a square.
Can you cut it up into four identical
pieces?

25. Building whole numbers As an easier variation on the 1969 problem, (see page 18) can you use the digits 1, 2, 3, 4, and 5, in any order, with the operations of addition, subtraction, multiplication, and division, to build the successive whole numbers? Here are a couple to start you off:

(These look harder when I write them out. Try just figuring them out mentally. It may help to write the digits down on five pieces of paper, and move the papers around as you juggle the numbers.)

26. Equal candy for all Brian has proposed that he, David, and Kevin split their candy evenly and, since they have all the candy and he has money, he has agreed to pay them proportionately. He suggested a nickel per bar, since that was the going rate at the store, but David pointed out that this would get them involved in fractional parts of cents. So Brian reluctantly agreed to six cents per candy bar. If David contributed five bars and Kevin three, how should they divide the money?

27. Fresh fish The head of a fish is four inches long. The tail is as long as the head and half the body. The body is as long as the head and tail together. What is the over-all length of the fish?

28. Remains of a division problem Fill in the missing digits here so that you have a very proper long-division example.

From long ago and far away

1. Short cut to addition As a small boy in a German elementary school, Karl Friedrich Gauss is said to have discovered a quick method for adding the numbers from 1 to 100, thereby completing in a few minutes an assignment that the teacher had hoped would keep the class busy while he had a nap. Suppose your teacher told you to add the numbers from 1 to 100. Could you find a short cut?

Gauss went on to become one of the great mathematicians. How do things look for you?

2. Some different differences One problem that intrigued Karl Friedrich Gauss went something as follows: Write down the digits 1 through 8 in order:

1 2 3 4 5 6 7 8

Underneath these write the digits 1 through 8 in such an order that all eight pairs will have different sums and all eight pairs will have different differences.

Gauss said there were seventy-two solutions, but actually there are ninety-six. How many can you find?

3. Eight queens Related to that last puzzle about the eight digits is that of placing eight queens on a chessboard in such a way that none can take any of the others. Again, there are ninety-six solutions.

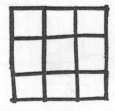

4. 3-by-3 magic You probably have seen that simplest of all magic squares, but just in case you haven't, the problem goes like this: place the numbers 1 through 9 in the square:

so that every row, column, and diagonal gives the same sum.

If you have done this before, go on to the next puzzles, which are variations on this basic magic square.

(This puzzle is in the "From long ago and far away" section because the magic square was known to the Chinese possibly as early as 2200 B.C. Legend has it that an emperor found it inscribed on the shell of a tortoise. The Muslims, who were much interested in mathematics, also were intrigued by the magic square. It was regarded by some as a good luck symbol, and doctors sometimes had it drawn on the soles of a patient's feet.)

5. Given two entries Here's an easy variation on the magic square. The digits you use to build a magic square need not be in order. Try completing this one in which the smallest number you use is 9 and the largest is 25. They could be placed like this:

6. A square triangular total This one is a bit tougher, just so you won't get bored. Let the magic total this time be 36—that number which is both triangular and square. I'll give you two of the entries in the magic square.

You complete the square.

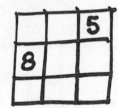

7. Triangular magic square As you noticed, the rows, columns, and diagonals in the first magic square all total 15, which is a triangular number. Can you make up a magic square in which each row, column, and diagonal totals 21, the next triangular number?

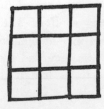

8. A magic domino square ... or a "domino magic square."
Can you arrange the dominoes shown below into a four-by-
four square so that each row, column, and diagonal will have
the same total? (Naturally you must regard each end of a
domino as a separate entry in your magic square.)

($\frac{2}{4}$, $\frac{4}{5}$, $\frac{4}{6}$, $\frac{5}{5}$, $\frac{5}{6}$, $\frac{3}{4}$, $\frac{3}{6}$, $\frac{6}{6}$)

Would it help if I told you that the magic total is 19?

9. Find the cubes G. H. Hardy, the British mathematician, tells about going to visit Ramanujan, the self-taught Indian mathematician, in the hospital. He told Ramanujan that he had hoped to have an interesting license number from the taxi to report, but was disappointed. Ramanujan asked what the number was and, when Hardy told him, said immediately, "Why, that is the smallest number that can be represented in two ways as the sum of two cubes."

What was the number on the taxi's license plate?

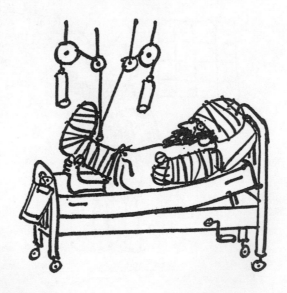

10. From the Ladies' Diary When I first ran across the magazine *Ladies' Diary*, I was surprised to find that, despite its name, it contained a goodly number of interesting mathematical puzzles and problems. Here's one, in poem form, from a 1707 issue:

If to my age there added be
One half, one third and three times three.
Six score and ten the sum, you'd see.
Pray find out what my age may be.

11. A blockhead counts bunnies Back about the year 1200 there lived a mathematician named Leonardo of Pisa, who is best remembered now as Fibonacci. Fibonacci traveled quite a bit, learning mathematics from the Muslims, studying the methods of calculations used by the Indians, and engaging in mathematics contests with other mathematicians. Because of these activities the nickname "The Traveler" was attached to his name. But, it seems, the word for "traveler" also meant "blockhead," and so he was described by writers of later centuries.

Fibonacci solved many problems in his time and wrote several books that were important in the development of mathematics in Europe, but the problem that brought him lasting fame may seem a strange one to be taken seriously by a great mathematician. It goes something like this:

If we begin with one pair of rabbits, and assume that each
   pair will produce another pair each month after the first,
   how many pairs of rabbits will we have after twelve months?
(We are assuming also that no rabbits die during that year.)

The pattern of numbers that gives the number of pairs of rabbits at the end of each month has become a very well-known pattern, called the "Fibonacci sequence."

Can you figure out the pattern that gives the number of rabbits?

12. The Fibonacci numbers Those numbers that Leonardo of Pisa said gave a solution to his bunny problem are:

1, 1, 2, 3, 5, 8, 13, 21, 34

and so on, have a tremendous number of remarkable properties.

For example, take any three consecutive numbers; square the middle one, and compare the result with the product of the other two.

Or, add up the first six numbers and compare the sum with the eighth number. Add the first twelve and look for a number in the sequence that is related to it.

The possibilities here seem to be almost unlimited. How many properties can you discover? I find that it helps to write out the first fifteen or twenty Fibonacci numbers, which is easily done, since each term is just the sum of the two just before it.

As a further hint, try cubing 8 $(8\cdot8\cdot8=512)$ and 5 $(5\cdot5\cdot5=125)$ and 3 $(3\cdot3\cdot3=27)$. Now:

$$512+125-27=610$$

which is a Fibonacci number.

Will this always happen?

1
1
2
3
5
8
13
21
34
55
89
144
233
377
610
987
1597
2584

13. Lightning addition Since you have all those Fibonacci numbers written down, you might as well impress your friends with your mental arithmetic. Tell them to cut off the series at any number, and you'll add up the preceding numbers immediately.

For example, if they cut off at 610, you can say that the sum of the numbers up to and including 610 is 1596.

Or, if the cut-off number is 144, the sum is 376. Isn't it?

From long ago and far away   49

14. From an Indian mathematician Problems from the Hindus have been notably colorful. Take this one, from the ninth-century mathematician Mahavira:

"A powerful unvanquished excellent black snake, which is 32 hastas in length, enters into a hole at the rate of 7½ angulas in 5/14 of a day; and in the course of ¼ of a day, its tail grows by 2¾ angula. O ornament of arithmeticians, tell me by what time this same serpent enters fully into the hole."

Now, I have been unable to find the relationship between a hasta and an angula—so suppose I make this easy by saying that thirty-two hastas shall be equal to ten angulas.

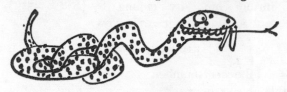

15. An archaeological problem Professor Digzaplenty, the noted archaeologist, has discovered the remains of an ancient civilization in the interior of South America. He is able to translate the language but has run into mathematical difficulties. Here is one problem, written out on a clay tablet, which was evidently an exercise from some struggling young scholar:

A man has ℺ coconut trees, each producing ℧ coconuts. How many coconuts will he get in all?

The professor does know that the ancient people used a positional scale of notation. And he has found a part of another tablet with the following inscriptions:

Say quickly, then, how many coconuts?

16. Anyone for B-B's? "We'll melt down these British cannon balls and make musket shot of them," thundered Lieutenant Obediah Dickinson, of the Continental Army. "Diameter must be twenty times musket size, and that'll make a handsome parcel of musket shot. Don't have any cannon, anyway."

Say quickly, O patriotic arithmetician, about how many musket balls will one cannon ball make?

17. Dots, lines, and rhymes Here's a dots and lines puzzle from an 1821 book by John Jackson, and he even wrote it in verse:

Your aid I want, nine trees to plant
    In rows just half a score.
And let there be in each row three.
    Solve this: I ask no more.

18. A military version There are many problems similar to the last one. One of these has the sergeant bark at his ten men: "Aw right, you guys, line up in five rows of four men each."

Now, sergeants that I have known would say such a thing only when they were much confused. And sergeants are not often confused. But can you show the men how to line up?

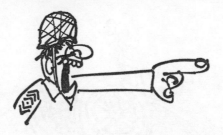

19. The age of Diophantus The mathematician Diophantus worked at Alexandria when that city was the greatest center of learning in the Western world. His work has become very famous, but practically nothing is known of his life. In fact, all the information we have is given in a puzzle that was written down about the year 500:

Diophantus' boyhood lasted one-sixth of his life; his beard grew after one-twelfth more; after one-seventh more he married, and his son was born five years later; the son lived to half his father's age, and the father died four years after his son.

How long did Diophantus live?

From long ago and far away

20. From the books of Diophantus   Many of Diophantus' problems make rather interesting puzzles. Try this one: Divide 100 into two parts such that one-fourth of the one part is twenty more than one-sixth of the second part.

21. Another Diophantine puzzle If you liked the last little problem, try this one, also from one of Diophantus' books, by the way: From both 100 and 20 subtract the same number so that one remainder will be six times as large as the other remainder.

22. Pythagorean number patterns Fifteen is the magic number of that simplest of magic squares, but 15 is really considered a triangular number, since it can be represented by dots in the shape of a regular triangle.

This kind of dot representation of numbers goes back to the Pythagoreans, a secret society that began in the sixth century B.C. The Pythagoreans believed that everything could be explained in terms of numbers.

Of course there are also square numbers, such as:

Can you find a number that is both square and triangular?

23. Plato's cubes Plato, the philosopher, has started many mathematical traditions. Among them is a problem about a monument consisting of a large cube standing in the center of a square plaza. The large cube is made up of small cubes and the plaza is paved with small cubes of the same size. There are the same number of small cubes in the plaza as there are in the large cube.

Legends associate the problem with the following sketch, which should help you figure out how many small cubes there are in the large one.

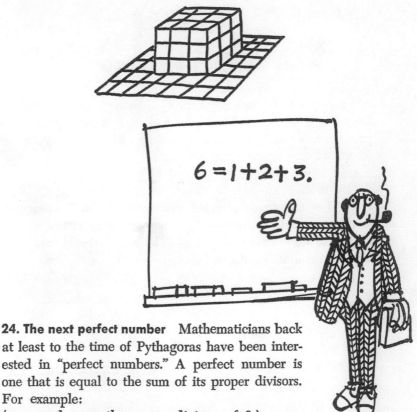

$$6 = 1 + 2 + 3.$$

24. The next perfect number Mathematicians back at least to the time of Pythagoras have been interested in "perfect numbers." A perfect number is one that is equal to the sum of its proper divisors. For example:

(1, 2, and 3 are the proper divisors of 6.)

Can you find the next perfect number?

Build your own

1. The tower of Benares For this puzzle you need a piece of wood, three pieces of dowling, and five cardboard disks of different sizes. Actually you can use a variety of materials, but you should be able to make such an arrangement as this:

What is the smallest number of moves you need to transfer the disks from the left-hand post to the right-hand post . . . if you can move only one disk at a time and never place a disk on top of one smaller than it?

How many moves do you need to move six disks?

The problem is said to have originated in India, where, at the beginning of the world, certain monks at Benares were faced with such a problem . . . but involving sixty-four gold disks and three diamond pillars. The world would end when they had completed the switch.

2. Big trapezoids from little ones

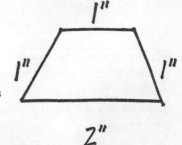

Now, it's easy to put together four trapezoids proportioned

like this to form another trapezoid having the same shape . . . isn't it?

But can you put together nine such trapezoids to form a trapezoid with the same shape? (That is, the top and sides are each just half as long as the bottom.)

Cut out nine trapezoids and try it.

3. Four squares take nine Trapezoids too hard to make? Here's an easy-to-construct basic piece:

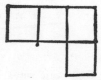

Can you put together nine of these to form a large figure of the same shape?

4. Saw a pyramid For a bit of variety on the business of cutting up the three-inch cube, suppose you try the same thing with a three-inch regular tetrahedron. (A tetrahedron has four triangular faces . . . and is very easy to build, if you think a model would help you on this problem. A floor plan appears below.) Anyway, you cut up the (blue, chartreuse, lavender) tetrahedron with parallel cuts one inch apart along each edge. "How" are the pieces painted?

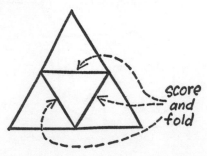

score
and
fold

5. A cubic cut-up Suppose you had a cube three inches along an edge and painted blue (or chartreuse . . . or whatever your favorite color happens to be). You cut this cube into one-inch cubes, with saw cuts parallel to the faces. How many faces of the one-inch cubes will be painted?

6. Little cubes from big ones Suppose your cube were four inches on an edge, similarly painted, and then cut up. How many painted faces will the little cubes have?

7. A multicolored cube Instead of daubing the same color of paint all over the cube, suppose you had six colors. In how many different ways can you paint the cube?

8. Illusions and delusions So that a picture of an object will appear real, an artist often has to distort the object—create an illusion.

Thus, for example, he draws railroad tracks like this:

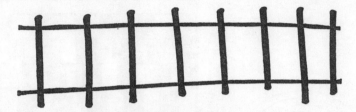

and says that they are parallel. and they do appear parallel. Or a teacher in school draws this:

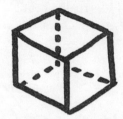

and you accept it as a "cube" . . . though there are no right angles . . . and the edges are not the same length.

But suppose I take that "cube"; change the dotted lines to solid; and . . . which is the "front" and which the "back"?

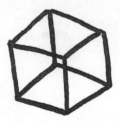

Maybe it's just a hexagon with some lines drawn in.

You have an optical illusion.

The optical illusion is not strictly a mathematical idea, but mathematical things lend themselves to this business.

Build your own   59

Are the lines across the figure parallel . . . or not parallel?
Look at the figure carefully!

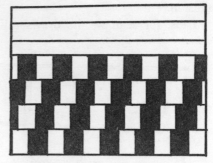

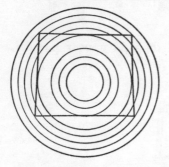

Are the sides of this figure
really bent?
Or is this a square?

Could this be a triangle . . .
with straight sides, that is?
Test them with a ruler.
But perhaps the ruler has a
kink in it.

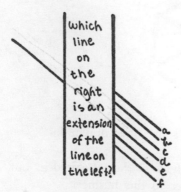

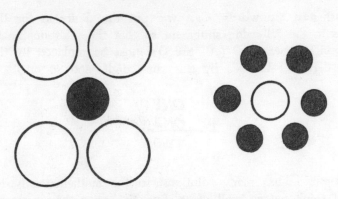

Which center circle is larger?

From these samples you can get ideas about the ingredients of optical illusions. Why not build some of your own?

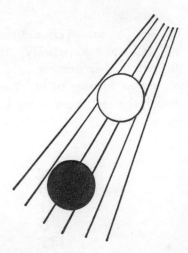

As a final optical puzzle . . . which circle is larger?

9. Just add the words Can you put the digits in for the letters in the following statement so that the addition makes sense in numbers too? (All the O's must be replaced by the same digit, all the N's by the same digit, and so on.)

$$
\begin{array}{r}
ONE \\
+\ ONE \\
\hline
TWO
\end{array}
$$

(This puzzle has many solutions, so the mathematically inclined think not so well of it. But 'tis easier than most. If you want a bit harder puzzle that has only one solution try the next. Or why not make up some of your own.)

$$
\begin{array}{r}
FORTY \\
TEN \\
+\ TEN \\
\hline
\\
SIXTY
\end{array}
$$

10. Up by one Tell a friend that you are going to give him ten numbers quickly. After each number he is to say the next higher number . . . quickly. Bet him that he won't get every number right. You might try the following list, though the real teaser is the last number—most people respond, "5000" to it.

74	216
17	1358
121	141
8	62
139	4099

11. Tangrams This puzzle-game came originally from China. H. E. Dudeney, who originated and collected many mathematical puzzles, suggests that there may be some mystery attached to the tangrams, for Chinese people refuse to talk about how the pieces were first used.

Anyway, there are seven pieces: two large triangles:

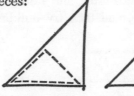

another triangle half that size:

and two more half the size of that one:

a square, which is equal to the two smallest triangles together:

and a rhomboid, also equal to two little triangles together:

Tangrams are available commercially, in plastic, but you can easily cut a set from quarter-inch plywood.

The idea is to arrange these seven pieces to form figures and designs:
a square:

                    a trapezoid:

or a K:

                                        the letter M:

how about a bird:

                    or a flower:

12. Some seventh-grade originals   You should be able to construct skeleton arithmetic puzzles. The trick is to give just enough information to make the puzzle challenging—and yet enough so that there is only one solution.

Here are a couple invented by seventh-grade students Chris Dain, Brenda Foster, and Robbin Rock, of Oswego, New York. Try these, and then try building one of your own.

$$
\begin{array}{r}
x \; \_ \; \overline{4} \\
\hline
2 \; \_ \; \_ \\
2 \; \_ \; \_ \\
\hline
\_ \; \_ \; 0 \; 8
\end{array}
\qquad
\begin{array}{r}
x \; \overline{8} \; \_ \\
\hline
6 \; \_ \; \_ \\
\_ \; \_ \; 2 \\
\hline
\_ \; \_ \; \_ \; 3
\end{array}
$$

(There are two solutions.)   (Also two solutions.)

$$
\begin{array}{r}
x \; \_ \; \_ \\
2 \; \_ \\
\hline
\_ \; \_ \; 7 \\
\_ \; 6 \\
\hline
9 \; \_ \; \_
\end{array}
$$

13. Blue and red exchange   To do this up fancy, you need a board with nine holes drilled in to a depth of about one-half inch. You also need eight pieces of dowling, each about one inch long, to fit into the holes loosely. Daub a little red paint on four pieces, and blue paint on the other four. Place the pieces as shown in the sketch.

The problem is to move the reds to where the blues are, and the blues to where the reds are—in the smallest possible number of moves. Rules for moving are as follows:

a) a piece may move one space of jump *one* other piece;

b) a piece may move only forward . . . never backward.

How many moves do you need?

I called this the "fancy" version. You can arrange two kinds of coins and get the same problem.

14. The Möbius strip Not really a puzzle—but this strip of paper behaves unexpectedly. Begin with a strip about twelve inches long and one inch wide. Draw a line lengthwise through the middle of the strip, and on both sides.

Now give the strip a half twist and glue the ends together. You now have a Möbius strip. Cut along that line you drew and see what happens.

Try making a similar cut through the pieces from the first cut. Or make another Möbius strip marked in thirds, and cut along these lines.

There are many possibilities—and some surprising results.

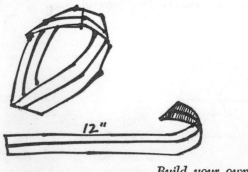

12"

15. Three-digit double reverse Begin with a three-digit number. Reverse the digits. Subtract the smaller from the larger. Now add this answer to the number you get by reversing its digits.

The answer is—well, you figure it out.

16. The hexaflexagon You begin with a strip of paper marked off into equilateral triangles like this:

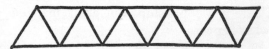

Make your first fold back (you'll find that it helps to score the lines of the folds):

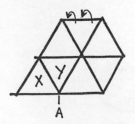

Your second fold is like this . . . again back, behind the rest of the piece: And, finally, fold triangle X on top of triangle Y, and paste these together.

When the paste is dry, flex the flexagon to turn up a new set of faces.

You can dramatize the fact that this flexagon has three "sides" by painting them different colors . . . or at least by numbering 1's on one set of six triangles, 2's on another set, and 3's on the third set.

17. Two for a pyramid

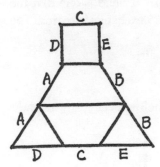

Make two pieces like that one shown from light cardboard. Tape together with masking tape, and you have a surprisingly tricky puzzle. The idea is to put the two pieces together to form a regular tetrahedron (a pyramid with a triangular base).

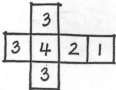

18. One, two, three, four cubes

This puzzle consists of four cubes. I have shown the numbering schemes on the layouts. Assemble four such cubes and number them as shown. Then try to arrange them so that along each side you have the digits 1, 2, 3, and 4.

19. Only-bet-on-a-sure-thing department Occasionally I arrange a small bet with a student in one of my classes. Of course I try to make sure that I am betting on as close to a sure thing as possible. This is the only way to bet. Here is an example of those "good" bets—not really sure things, but they will do until sure things come along.

If you know a poker player, here's a bet that he will probably take: What are the chances of making five "pat" poker hands out of twenty-five cards dealt? (A pat hand is one that the player would play as dealt to him . . . no exchange of cards. The possible pat hands are:

1. full house—three of a kind and a pair;
2. flush—five cards of a suit;
3. straight—five cards in sequence.)

You might experiment with this a bit before seeing my remarks in the answer section.

20. Bet on the loser Here's a baseball bet that is almost a sure winner. Choose the best team and the poorest team in the major leagues. Offer to bet that the poor team's scores for the season added together will give a larger total than the best team's scores multiplied together.

Do you see why you can hardly lose this bet?

21. Happy birthday Would you bet for or against this proposition: Of your class at school, two people have the same birthday.

If there are more than twenty-three people in your class, better bet for the proposition. The odds will be with you. If there are thirty or more people in your class, the bet gets close to a sure thing.

22. License numbers The question is whether or not, out of twenty cars, there will be at least two for which the last two digits of the license numbers are the same.

This might seem a rather unlikely thing to happen, but check a few times before you propose the bet to someone. It's almost a sure thing that two licenses out of twenty will have the same last two digits.

Puzzles and patterns

1. To make a thousand Once upon a time I saw this problem posed: Insert addition signs in the proper places among these 8's to make a total of 1000.

$$8\;8\;8\;8\;8\;8\;8\;8$$

Now this is not very difficult, but you can work on that for a starter.

And then, of course, you'll want to try making 1000 with seven 7's. (You can't line them up as I've done with the eight 8's, but you can build 1000 with seven 7's.)

Or how about nine 9's?

Or six 6's?

Making 1000 with five 5's is a bit trickier, but it can be done.

I can't seem to do it with four 4's, but don't let that stop you from trying.

Or you can find some fancy ways in which to build 1000 with eight 8's.

$$8\;8\;8\;8\;8\;8\;8\;8$$

2. Striking time If it takes eight seconds for a clock to strike eight, how long will it take the same clock to strike twelve?

3. Given enough rope Suppose you had a rope long enough to just reach around the earth—say, twenty-five thousand miles—and neglect little obstacles such as mountains, oceans, etc. Now lengthen the rope by one yard and stretch it out. How far above the surface of the earth would the rope be?

4. A set of weights If you were going to choose five weights that would enable you to weigh whole numbers of grams, which five would you choose so that you could weigh one, two, three, etc., grams up to the total of the five weights?

5. Package deal If a cork and bottle together cost fifty-five cents, and the bottle costs fifty cents more than the cork, how much does each cost?

6. The number wheel Arrange the numbers 1 through 11 in the figure shown below so that the sum of all lines of three will be the same.

7. Division by age Brian and Jeff were walking along the road, with Brian's younger brother, Rob, tagging along. They found some money on the road and were trying to decide how to split it up. Jeff pointed out that, if the money were all in dimes, the number of dimes would equal the sum of their ages.

"Okay," said Brian, "why not divide it according to our ages? Let's get it changed into dimes."

So Brian got one more dime than Jeff got, and seven more than Rob, while Jeff got twice as many dimes as did Rob.

How much money did they find?

8. They're off and running John beats Peter in a mile race by thirty seconds. But if John gives Peter one-fifth-mile handicap, Peter wins by thirty seconds. How long does it take John to run a mile?

9. The first shall be last Working out the decimal expansion of a fairly common fraction should help you with this one.

$$\underline{abcdef} \times 3 = \underline{bcdefa}$$

and

$$\underline{cdefab} \times 3 = \underline{defabc}$$

(The a's stand for the same digit throughout, as do the b's, c's, and so on.)

The First Shall be last

10. Reverse by multiplying For a bit of a twist to the missing-digit problems, try these, where a simple multiplication reverses the digits.

$$\underline{a}\ \underline{b}\ \underline{c}\ \underline{d} \times 4 = \underline{d}\ \underline{c}\ \underline{b}\ \underline{a}$$

$$\underline{p}\ \underline{q}\ \underline{r}\ \underline{s} \times 9 = \underline{s}\ \underline{r}\ \underline{q}\ \underline{p}$$

11. Bear Color Here's an easy one, but look out for the follow-up problem . . . it's a bit tricky: A man walks ten miles due south, then ten miles due east and sees a bear. Then he walks ten miles due north and is back where he started. What color is the bear?

(The follow-up problem is on page 88, but answer this one first.)

12. Skeleton multiplication There are a few digits missing in this multiplication problem. Fill them in so that the problem makes good mathematical sense.

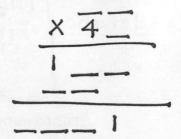

13. A balancing act If the two combinations of cylinders, cubes, and spheres balance, as shown, what should you place on the right side of the pan balance in order to equalize the one cylinder, as indicated in the third sketch?

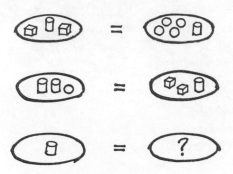

14. The tin half Since the scales are already drawn and you are into the weighing business, consider another old favorite. Of eight apparently identical coins, one is known to be counterfeit and slightly lighter than the others. How would you, with just two weighings on the pan balance, locate the counterfeit coin?

15. Business merger Two boys are selling tomatoes to make a little spending money. Each opens business with sixty tomatoes. One sells his at three for twenty cents, and takes in

four dollars. The other sells his sixty at two for fifteen cents and grosses $4.50. They decide to combine their efforts the next day, and again they begin with 120 tomatoes. Figuring that three for twenty cents and two for fifteen cents makes five for thirty-five cents, they decide to sell them at seven cents each. At the end of the day they have $8.40 instead of the $8.50 of the previous day. What happened to that extra dime?

16. The signs are lacking Just fill in the signs to have the statements make sense in all directions.

8		7		12		44
4		3		4		28
7		5		6		12
25		9		10		6

17. Pick your own numbers

Last puzzle too easy? I'll supply the signs. Just fill in the numbers.

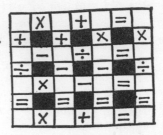

There remains only the complete "do-it-yourself." I'll even let you furnish your own square.

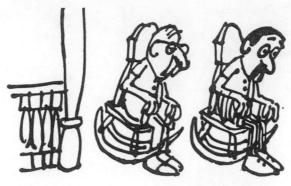

18. Toward easier multiplication

Long multiplication need not be such a chore. Try this one:

$$142857 \times 326451$$

or this:

$$76{,}923 \times 68{,}275$$

19. Age-old problem Joe is twice as old as Harry was when Joe was Harry's age. When Harry is as old as Joe is now, the sum of their ages will be 100. How old is each?

20. Guess a number

Take half a number
    And add to seven;
Then triple all this
And subtract eleven.

But that number plus twenty
    Gives answer the same.
This method's neater
    But much too tame.

21. Your favorite digit The following problem is a well-known one that you may have seen before. I mention it only because

I am going to suggest that you invent other problems like it. Multiply the following:

$$\begin{array}{r} 12345679 \\ \times\ 18 \\ \hline \end{array} \qquad \begin{array}{r} 12345679 \\ \times\ 27 \\ \hline \end{array}$$

$$\begin{array}{r} 12345679 \\ \times\ 36 \\ \hline \end{array} \qquad \begin{array}{r} 12345679 \\ \times\ 45 \\ \hline \end{array}$$

If you see the pattern in these multiplications, can you write other combinations that will give answers like these?

22. Salary increase Which would you choose: a $400 raise each year or a $100 raise each half-year, assuming that the starting salaries are the same?

23. The Latin square Can you place numbers 1, 2, 3, and 4 in a four-by-four array so that each row, each column, and each diagonal contains all four digits?

The idea is to make an array such as this:

1	2	3	4
2	3	4	1
3	4	1	2
4	1	2	3

but of course the diagonals here are not satisfactory.

24. Face-card double square For a small problem, related to the four-by-four Latin square, try arranging the face cards (jacks, queens, kings, aces) from a deck into a four-by-four array such that no row, column, or diagonal contains more than one card of any suit or rank.

25. A military square Leonhard Euler, one of the outstanding mathematicians of the eighteenth century, investigated the six-by-six version of the double Latin square problem. He stated the problem as follows: Arrange thirty-six officers, six from each of six ranks and drawn from six regiments, in a square formation, so that each row and each column contains an officer of each rank and from each regiment.

I hasten to add that this problem is unsolvable, but the five-by-five version can be solved.

Can't it?

Again, you might use playing cards to simulate the officers.

26. Know your p's and q's

Twice the sum of p and q
  Equals p times q divided by 2.
With this you'll need just one fact more
  P is equal to q times 4.

Quickly now!
Look alive!
P is _____
Q is _____

27. One long line
Can you trace the following figure without lifting your pencil from the page and without retracing any part of the figure?

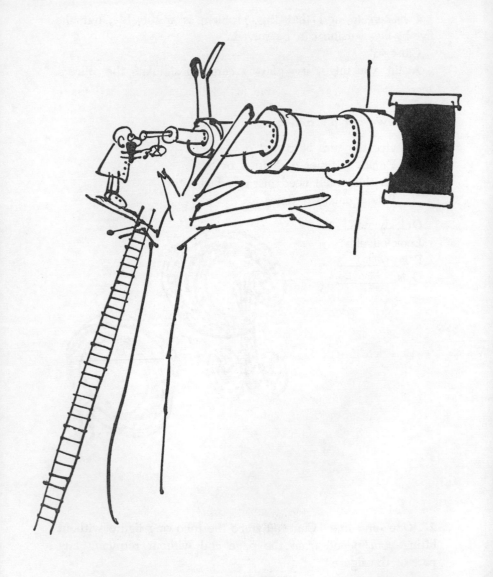

28. Even sevens What numbers under 1000 leave a remainder of 1 when divided by 2, 3, 4, 5, or 6, but are evenly divided by 7?

29. Check your Christmas card list In a class there are twice as many girls as boys. Each girl sends a Christmas card to every other girl, to every boy, and to the teacher. Each boy sends a card to every other boy, to every girl, and to the teacher. In all there are nine hundred cards sent. How many boys are there in the class?

30. Simplify by complicating As you have probably discovered, you cannot trace this rather simple diagram without either lifting your pencil from the page or going twice over part:

But if I add some lines and complicate the drawing a bit:

you can trace it with one continuous mark . . . and no re-tracing.

Can't you?

31. Pie for eight Cut a pie into eight pieces with only three cuts. (And you aren't allowed to cut it in half and place one half on top of the other. This is a cream pie!)

32. Match this arithmetic Add five more matches to these and make nine:

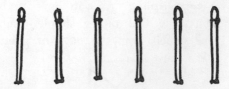

1. John loves ~~Mary~~ Kay John is twice as old as Mary was when John was as old as Mary is now. How old is each?

2. The arrangement makes sense Arrange six pennies in three straight rows, each having four pennies in it.

3. To catch a thief A thief is twenty-eight steps ahead of an officer and takes nine steps while the officer takes five. But two of the officer's steps are equal to five of the thief's. In how many steps will the officer catch the thief?

4. What happened to "west"? Back on page 76 there was an easy puzzle about a bear. And, of course, the expected answer was that he was a polar bear, for the hunter must have started from the North Pole.

But if I left out the part about the bear, there are other possibilities for this puzzle.

Where else, on the earth, could a person walk ten miles south, then ten miles east, and, finally, ten miles north and be back where he started?

5. The new arithmetic "I don't like this arithmetic," announced Jenny. "I'm going to invent my own."

"Okay," I agreed, "but keep it simple—so that we other poor people will be able to understand it."

She thought a minute and then announced, "2 and 5 equals 17; 8 and 7 equals 31."

"You better have a special sign," I pointed out, "so we'll know this is not ordinary arithmetic."

After a bit of mumbling to herself Jenny wrote:

$$2 \text{ T } 5 = 17$$
$$7 \text{ T } 8 = 31$$

"Is this base 10?" I asked hopefully.
"Oh yes," said she. "You said to keep it simple.
Have you figured out Jenny's system? What should

$$\text{and} \quad \begin{array}{c} 4 \text{ T } 5 \\ 3 \text{ T } 9 \end{array}$$

equal in this new arithmetic?

6. Last flight of a bumblebee Two trains are approaching each other on the same track, one traveling at fifty miles per hour, and the other at thirty miles per hour. When they are forty miles apart, a bumblebee takes off from the faster train and flies straight down the track to the other train at a speed of sixty miles per hour. Without stopping to rest, he turns around and heads back. He flies back and forth, to be smashed, so the story goes, between the trains when they collide.

How far does the bee fly?

7. Pinned up Fourteen clothespins are strung on a line at seven-foot intervals. How far is it from the first pin to the last?

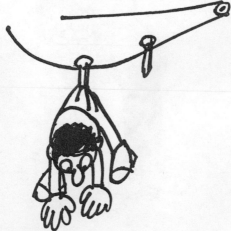

8. To the root of the problem The cube root of a certain number is ten times the fourth root. What is the number?

9. Reverse multiplication reverses multiplication This may sound like a play on words (and it is), but the real puzzle involves doing just what the title says. Can you find two two-digit numbers such that when you reverse them and then multiply your answer is just the reverse of the product of the first two numbers?

10. A fifty-per-cent complication If that last "reversals' reversal" was too easy, try the same problem with three-digit numbers.

I'll give you a clue to one such combination:

$$\underline{a}\ \underline{b}\ \underline{c}\ \times\ \underline{c}\ \underline{c}\ \underline{b}$$

11. A bargain's a bargain A man bought an antique whazzit for 90 percent of its "book" value and sold it for 25 percent more than its book value, thereby turning a neat profit of $105. What was the book value of this fine whazzit?

12. The slow freight Two trains start at the same time, one from Punxsutawney heading for Zelienople, and one from Zelienople heading for Punxsutawney. If they arrive at their destinations one hour and four hours after passing, what are their relative rates of running?

13. Multiplication equals addition It is very obvious that 2 plus 2 is equal to 2 times 2 ... but is there a number you can add to 3 and multiply by 3 to get the same result?

14. Folding money A man went to a bank to cash a check

for $240. He asked for the money in tens, fives, and ones—three times as many five-dollar bills as tens, and five times as many ones as tens. How many of each did the teller give him?

15. Globs a-doubling The Glob is a relative of the Shmoo (smaller but having that same roly-poly appearance). A Glob, under proper conditions of temperature, pressure, and humidity, will double in size and then divide in two every minute. In fact, if you place a Glob in a bucket and place in a warm, moist spot, after an hour you will have a bucketful of Globs.

When would the bucket be half full?

16. No singles Suppose you were a teller in a bank and a customer wanted a check for sixty-three dollars cashed in six bills, none of them ones. Can you satisfy this request?

(You run into all kinds of strange requests in a bank.)

17. The mathematical preparation of chocolate milk Jenny was mixing herself a glass of chocolate milk. "You sure have enough chocolate syrup in the glass," remarked Jeff, who then found a glass for his own drink.

"Only a third of a glass of syrup," pointed out Jenny. "And you're sure taking your share."

"I guess I have only about one-fourth of a glass," estimated Jeff piously.

"But your glass is twice as big!"

"Tell you what," said Jeff after they both had mixed milk and syrup in their glasses. "Let's combine them in a pitcher, and then split the whole amount."

While Jenny is trying to decide whether or not this arrangement is to her advantage, can you say what part of that combined mixture would be syrup?

18. A domestic problem There remains an important question related to the chocolate milk problem: Who will wash the pitcher?

19. A real estate deal "I'll give you a real good deal on this piece of land—sight unseen," proposed the real estate hustler to the man from the city. "Just $500 for the whole piece . . . and look how many acres you get."

"Just a minute," said the customer, "till I figure out how many acres I will be getting. My math's not as good as it used to be. How many square feet are there in an acre, anyway?"

"43,560," replied the real estate man promptly, as if he had been through this a few times.

Can you help the man from the city? Is he really getting quite a bargain here?

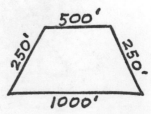

20. Small change "I have $2.55 in nickels and dimes," his uncle told Ben. "And three more nickels than dimes. If you can tell me how many of each I have, I'll feed the dimes to your Hungry Dog bank."

Can you help Ben out?

21. Share the work Suppose Wendy can do a particular job in three hours, while Amy can finish the same job in two hours. How long would the job take if they worked on it together?

(When I posed this problem to Amy and Wendy, Wendy said, right away, "It would still take three hours. She'd just read a magazine and let me do all the work." But for the sake of the problem, suppose both girls worked together as hard as they work separately—and didn't get in each other's way.)

22. The walk'll do you good I have already covered one-third of the distance from South Boondocks to Boondock Junction . . . and when I walk another two miles I will be halfway there.

How far is it from South Boondocks to Boondock Junction?

23. The shifting coins Line up four pennies and four dimes (different color poker chips or almost any other easily moved pieces will do nicely) as shown.

You must move two adjacent coins together . . . and this is the only kind of move permitted. Can you, in four moves, rearrange the line-up so that like coins are together?

24. Up and down . . . a perfect square A perfect square is a number formed by multiplying a whole number by itself. What perfect square, when turned upside down, is still a perfect square?

25. Symmetrical landscaping Brian's father sent him out in the yard with a shovel and six trees to plant. "Be sure to plant them in three rows with three trees in each row," his father told him.

"Don't you mean two rows with three trees in each row?" inquired Brian.

"No," replied his father, "I mean just what I said."

How should Brian arrange the trees?

26. Woodcutting Two men working together can saw five cords of wood per day, or they can split eight cords of wood that has been sawed. How many cords of wood must they saw so that they will be occupied the rest of the day in splitting it?

27. How many dominoes? The usual set of dominoes includes all the combinations from a double blank to a double six. Quickly now—and without counting a set—how many dominoes are there in a set if they are all different?

You may have been ready for that one. I'll step up the problem a bit. There are sets of dominoes which go up to the double nine piece. How many dominoes are there in such a set?

28. Move-a-match With eleven matches you can state the following problem:

which, of course, does not make good mathematical sense. Can you move just one match and change this to an acceptable mathematical statement?

29. The L-shaped pennies I have six pennies arranged in an L-shape . . . four in the vertical row and three in the horizontal line. Can you move just one penny and have two lines of four each?

30. Making little ones out of big ones If I can cut a four-foot piece of two-by-six into one-foot pieces in four minutes, how long will it take me to cut a five-foot piece of two-by-six into one-foot pieces?

1. Guess his numbers Tell a friend to start with a number larger than 1 but less than 10. (And he is not to tell you what that number is.)

Have him double that.

     Then he must add 1.

          And multiply by 5.

Now tell him to add another number less than 10 . . . and tell you the total.

Mentally subtract 5 from the total he gives you . . .

and you will have a number whose digits are those he chose, or else one of you has made a mistake in arithmetic.

For example, if he began with 3 and then picked 5, you should end with 35.

2. From whence he started

Just so you can keep your friend guessing,
Here's a variation
On that last trick.

Begin with any number.
Add 3.
Double that result.
Subtract 2.
Take half of this.
Subtract 2 again.

You are back where you started.
If all the arithmetic went well.

3. To the same end These steps will bring everyone to the same number, regardless of where they begin.

> Pick any number.
> Multiply it by 3.
> Add 7.
> Add the number you started with.
> Add 5.
> Divide by 4.
> Subtract the number you started with.
>
> Your answer is "3."

4. Build your own Tricks like these last three are easy to make up. You can complicate them, or simplify, to suit your audience (and your own talents, of course). Why not try your hand at it?

But be sure to test your ideas first.

And watch for goofs in arithmetic!

5. 100 wins Two people can play. They may use numbers 1 through 10, taking turns adding a number. A running total is kept . . . and the player who makes that total an even 100 wins.

There is a strategy that will make you a winner every time.

6. 100 loses This is a variation on the game I just described, but the player who makes the score equal to or greater than 100 loses.

7. From 100 to 0 You can turn around those two games just mentioned. Begin with 100. The two players take turns subtracting any number from 1 through 10. In one version the player wins who makes the score zero. In the other version he loses.

Of course, once you have discovered the winning system, you will want to move from one version of the game to another. Keeps your opponent off balance.

You need not make the score 100 or zero. Just for a change of pace, make the winning (or losing) total 50, and let the players use only 1 through 6.

8. 100 in the cards For still another version of this 100 game, lay out, face up, three each of the aces through 10's of a deck of cards. Then two players alternate at picking up a card. The score is the running total of the numbers on the chosen cards. The player who makes the score an even 100 wins.

9. Guess the dice You can tell the result of a roll of the dice without ever looking at them. Ask a friend to roll a pair of dice but not let you see what numbers show. Tell him to multiply the number on one of the dice by 5. Then add 7, double the result, and add in the number on the second die. When he tells you this final result, subtract 14 and you'll know what the dice said. The first digit of your answer is the number on the first die; the second digit is the number on the second die.

10. The dice'll never tell If the two-dice trick fails to impress your audience, bring out another die and try this one. (This trick makes them do a little arithmetic too, so make sure they don't goof.)

Tell your friend to roll the three dice, write down the top numbers in some order, but not tell you. Then have him write down, again secretly and in the same order, the numbers on the bottoms of the three dice. Suppose the dice say:

Your friend writes down:

325,452

Have him divide this number by 37. Then have him divide that result by 3 and tell you the result.

You subtract 7 from the number he gives you, and then divide by 9. The digits of this number will be the numbers on the tops of the dice.

11. Even 'em up Begin with three piles of matches having eleven matches in pile A, seven in B, and six in C. You can move matches from one pile to another, but only as many matches as there are in the pile to which you are moving. For example, you can move either seven matches from A to B; six from A to C; or six from B to C. What is the smallest number of moves you need in order to even out the piles at eight matches each?

12. Numerical ticktacktoe

Use the same framework as for ticktacktoe, but one player has the odd numbers, 1, 3, 5, 7, 9, and the other, the evens, 2, 4, 6, 8, 10. Each in turn writes one of his numbers in a square. The object of the game is to make a row, column, or diagonal total 15. The player who does that wins the game.

13. 3-D number ticktacktoe Why stop at a simple ticktacktoe? For a three-dimensional version you need three arrays:

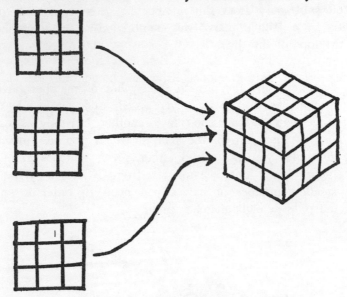

and the numbers 1 through 27. (We'll spot the odds an extra number.) Let the winning total be 42.

Some of the diagonals may be a bit hard to keep track of. For example:

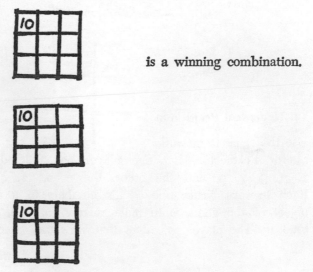

is a winning combination.

14. Guess a birthday This little trick will impress only someone you don't know very well. In particular, you must not know when his birthday is.

Have him begin with the number of the month of his birthday (1 for January, 2 for February, and so on). Have him multiply this by 5, and then tell him to tack a 3 on the end of these numbers. Now, he should add 12, "since there are twelve months in the year." Tell him to double this result. Lastly have him add in the day of the month on which he was born, and then give you the end result of all these calculations.

Subtract 30 from the number he gives you, and you have his birthday. For example, if his birthday is September 26, your number will be 926—assuming, of course, that neither you nor he made any mistakes in arithmetic.

15. Lightning calendar addition Tell a friend to draw a square around nine numbers on a page of a calendar, without showing you the numbers he enclosed. Ask him to tell you the smallest number of the nine.

Quickly add 8 and multiply by 9 and give him that result as the sum of the nine numbers in his square.

Naturally, this trick loses its impact if you are slow about the mental arithmetic, or, horrors, if you make a mistake.

16. A calendar prediction The last calendar trick may not be convincing, but this one should take in all of your audience.

Have one person draw a square around sixteen numbers on a calendar page. Glance at the square and write down a number, which you tell your audience will be the sum of four numbers they will determine.

Now, have one spectator circle one of these sixteen numbers. Cross out the row and column containing that number. Have another spectator circle another number. Cross out the row and column that contain that number. Do the same for a third number, which another spectator picks.

There should be one number not crossed out. The sum of it and the three encircled numbers will be the number you wrote down at the beginning. This sum will be equal to twice the sum of two diagonally opposite corner numbers of the original square of sixteen, which should be that number you write down in the first place.

17. Galloping dice This trick with three dice isn't so elaborate as the last one (on page 108), but there is less arithmetic involved, so less chance of things going wrong.

Turn your back while a friend throws three dice. Tell him to add the numbers on the faces. Then tell him to pick up one die and add in the number on the bottom to the previous total. He should roll this same die again and add the number it now shows to the total.

Now, you turn around and call attention to the fact that you have no way of knowing which of the three cubes was used for the second roll. Note the total of the faces that show and mentally add 7 to it. Pick up the dice, shake them a bit, and announce the number you got when you added 7 to the total showing. This will be your friend's final total.

18. Docile dominoes If you have played domino games, you have probably noticed that when you lay out an entire set of twenty-eight pieces, matching the ends according to dots, the numbers on the ends of the chain will match. So, if one domino is removed from the set, and the others are matched up in a chain, the ends of the chain will match the numbers on the piece that has been removed.

But don't take my word for it . . . try it.

Anyway, this little bit of information is the basis for a trick with dominoes.

Secretly remove one domino from a set and note the numbers on it. Now, ask a friend to match up the remainder of the pieces in one long chain—as in regular play. Tell him that you can predict the numbers that will be on the ends of the chain. Then write down the numbers on the piece you removed. Sure enough, 'twill turn out just as you said.

He may ask for a repeat, figuring that the chain may always end this way. In which case, ease the one stolen piece back into the pile and remove another—but carefully.

19. Cards by the count Have a friend shuffle a deck of cards and place it on the table. Secretly note the card on the bottom of the deck and write this on a piece of paper. Place the paper face down and tell no one what is on it.

Deal out twelve cards on the table, face down. Ask your friend to touch any four. Turn up the touched cards, gather the others, and return them to the *bottom* of the pack. Let's say the four cards are a 3, a 6, a king, and an 8.

Now, you deal cards on top of each of the four, to bring each total up to ten. On the 3, for example, you deal and count, "4, 5, 6, 7, 8, 9, 10." Court cards count ten so you would deal none on top of the king.

Add the values of the four cards ... in this case the total is 27. Hand the pack to your friend and ask him to count to the twenty-seventh card. This turns out to be the one you noted on the paper.

Better practice this trick a few times before showing off in public.

20. A double deal Begin this card trick by having a friend (or volunteer from the audience if you really feel confident) cut a *small* number of cards from a deck. He should not tell you how many cards he has. Now, cut a larger number for yourself. (This "larger" is obviously a matter of judgment.) Count the cards to yourself—let's say there are twenty-two. Then announce something to the effect that, "I have as many cards as you have, plus five cards—and enough left to make seventeen."

Your friend counts his cards aloud. Let's say he has ten. Count off ten of your cards. Place five others aside, as you said you would. Continue counting from the cards you cut—11, 12, 13, 14, 15, 16, 17. Sure enough, the seventeenth card is your last one.

21. Your lucky card For those who favor the "new math" here is a card trick that depends on the intersection of sets, so they say. But you needn't worry about the technical language. It's a rather effective trick, anyway. You are "the magician."

The magician is seated at a table with four spectators and deals five cards to each, including himself. He asks each person to select mentally one card among the five, then he gathers up the hands and once more deals out the cards to form five piles. The magician picks up any pile that the others select, and fans the cards so that the faces are toward the spectators. He asks if anyone sees his card—the one he had chosen earlier. If so, the magician (without looking at the cards, of course) immediately pulls the chosen card from the five. He can repeat the procedure for each of the piles of five.

What you do: Gather the hands face down, beginning with the first person on your left and going around the table. Your own five cards go on top of the packet last. Redeal the cards. Any of the five piles can now be fanned. If spectator 2 sees his card, it will be in the second position of the five you are holding up. If the fourth person sees his card, it will be in the fourth position, and so on. Some of the redealt piles may have more than one of the chosen cards; some may have none.

22. Strictly subtraction If you begin with the four numbers:

12   8   2   11

and subtract each one in turn from the one next to it (always subtracting the smaller from the larger), you get:

4   6   9   1   (12−11)

Continue this process to get:

2	3	8	3
1	5	5	1
4	0	4	0
4	4	4	4
0	0	0	0

Do you always get down to a row of zeros? Does this same thing happen for sets of three or five numbers?

23. The patterns game This is probably the easiest of the "do-it-yourself" ideas. You need no equipment, and a minimum of mathematical background. One person thinks of a pattern, and the others try to guess his pattern by giving him numbers and noting his responses. For example, you give me "6," and I reply, "15." Then you give me "8," and I reply, "21."

See the pattern yet?

If not, you continue with, say, "10," to which I reply,

"27," and so on, until you guess the pattern. Then it is your turn to make up a pattern.

In this case, of course, I was just multiplying your number by 3, and then subtracting 3.

24. Patterns unlimited The only limit to the possibilities in this patterns game is your imagination, so go to it. In case you need a little start, or must play solitaire, here are a few patterns to guess:

your number	2	5	8	13	21
my number	9	21	33	53	85

your number	3	5	7	9	12
my number	12	30	56	90	156

your number	2	3	5	7	10
my number	5	10	26	50	101

25. A solitaire number game If there is no one around to try these other games on, here's a one-man affair: Take any number, say 57, and add the squares of its digits:

$$5^2 + 7^2 = 25 + 49 = 74$$

Now, add the squares of the digits of 74:

$$7^2 + 4^2 = 49 + 16 = 65$$

and

$$6^2 + 5^2 = 36 + 25 = 61$$

Continue this process and see what pattern develops. You might try it with three-digit numbers also.

26. The four fours A particular favorite of mine is the problem of arranging four 4's, and only four 4's, to build the whole numbers. You can use the signs for addition, subtraction, multiplication, and division, and square root—and decimal points. For example, $1 = \frac{4}{4} \times \frac{4}{4}$, and $2 = \frac{4}{4} + \frac{4}{4}$. You can build to 30 this way, though 19 seems to give a bit of trouble.

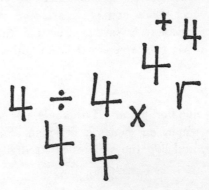

27. Nim Nim is a two-person game that can be completely and mathematically analyzed, but you can have a lot of fun without delving into the theory. And after you play the game a while you'll discover winning combinations.

For this game you need a goodly number of counters—

matches will do nicely. These are divided arbitrarily into a number of piles. The first player picks up matches from one pile. He may take the whole pile, but he must take at least one. Then the second player picks up matches from a pile. They alternate until all the counters are picked up. The winner is the player who picks up the last counter.

There are certain "safe" combinations. If you make sure that your opponent faces one of these, you can't lose. One such "safe" combination is seven, two, and five counters in three piles. I'll let you figure out some others by playing the game.

28. Wythoff's game

A variation on Nim was invented by W. A. Wythoff in 1910. In this game there are only two heaps of matches. A player may take counters from one or both piles. But if he takes from both, he must take the same number from each. The winner is the player who picks up the last match.

Again, there are certain "safe" combinations . . . such as (six, ten) or (eight, thirteen).

Answers

Puzzles are where you find them

1. Ten boys and twelve dogs should account for those legs and heads. You can jazz up the puzzle a bit by having a couple of boys hopping on one foot . . . or with a three-legged dog.

2. Just four miles back, with New York 324 miles away and Syracuse thirty-six. $9 \times 36 = 324$.

3. I kind of hate to fess up to this one, because people are generally disappointed. But all Mike was doing was counting the letters in the number words . . . three letters in "one," three in "two," and so on.

4. Here are a few more that may give you some clues on carrying this process further. I got as far as 28, but 29 seems a bit sticky.

$$(1 \cdot \sqrt{9} + 6) \div \sqrt{9} = 3$$
$$19 - (6 + 9) = 4$$
$$(1 \cdot 9 + 6) \div \sqrt{9} = 5$$

5. They must have twelve miles to go, for by increasing their pace from three to four miles per hour they cut an hour off the time. Since they had already come one-fifth of the way, the original plan must have been for fifteen miles.

6. Figure around the greens . . . and there had to be twelve green buttons. That means, twenty-four whites, eleven blues, and nineteen reds, for a total of sixty-six.

7. I find that a diagram like that below helps for such a puzzle as this. It provides for overlapping in categories, and all you have to do is write the proper numbers in the regions. Totaling up the regions, Jeff had thirty-four buttons.

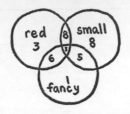

8. If two problems are worth 5 percent, one must be worth 2½ percent . . . or one-fortieth of the test.

9. David won sixty cents.

10. One-twelfth of the scholars must be between eleven and twelve, and, therefore, one-sixth between ten and eleven. This accounts for half the students (since one-fourth are over twelve). The other twelve people must be half the class . . . so the class numbers twenty-four.

11. After three hours and forty-five minutes of burning. But keep the candles out of the draft.

12. Holly had seven pieces; Heather had five.

13. Make a square with a quarter at each corner and a penny in each side.

14. The numbers must be 41 and 14. Try making up some of these on your own.

15. The octonary numbers are 52 and 25, of course, for in octonary arithmetic 52—25=25.

16. Since Jenny averaged fourteen pieces of candy a day (they really were quite small) she must have had more than fourteen on some days and less on others. Looks as if the numbers are 14, 14+3, 14+6, 14—3, and 14—6 . . . for a total of seventy.

17. There are sixty-four one-by-one squares, forty two-by-twos, thirty-six three-by-threes, twenty-five four-by-fours, and so on . . . for a grand total of 204 squares. Count 'em if you don't believe me.

18. My time spent on the bus was just twice that spent on the plane. That should be enough of a clue if you were stumped by this puzzle.

19. Frankie answered fourteen problems correctly, for seventy points, and lost them by answering the other ten incorrectly.

20. They should have driven 350 nails by nine-fifty, unless they got tired and slowed down the pace.

21. 'Tis now 8:10 P.M., and but a half hour ago 'twas only 7:40, and in another half hour you can make up another clock puzzle.

22. Meanwhile, there is this easy one . . . the time is 6:00 P.M.

Puzzles

1. The secret here is to make the third number such that it and the second number total 99999. Do the same for the fifth number to be matched with the fourth number. If your friend writes 23456, you respond 76543 . . . the sum is actually 99999. This means you can count on adding twice 99999, less 2, to the original number. This you accomplish in your prediction by sticking a 2 in front and subtracting 2 from the last digit. Now you give it a try. With any trick like this you will want to practice before you try to amaze people.

2. There are a number of ways with eleven coins . . . for example: three quarters, one dime, two nickels, five pennies; or, two quarters, eight nickels, one dime. With thirteen coins try seven dimes and six nickels.

3. Each man gets fifty-five acres' worth of grain, so Jingleheimer owes Smith for ten acres and Jones for forty-five. That is, the money should be split on a ten-to-forty-five basis, or twenty dollars for Smith and ninety dollars for Jones.

4. He just can't come down the mountain fast enough to average thirty m.p.h. for the trip.

5. The plate number must have been 19086. Turn it upside down and try. Then see if you can make up a similar puzzle.

6. Each boy does the work of two-thirds of a man.

7. $1\frac{9}{64}$ will do nicely, as will $1\frac{9}{95}$, $1\frac{5}{24}$ . . . and quite a few others.

8. The factors must be 27×84.

9. With a bit of number juggling, I come up with a=2, b=11, c=8, d=1, e=14, f=4, g=13, and h=5. How did you make out with this one?

10. Cut that 3″-by-8″ like so:

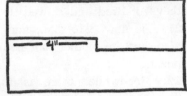

11. The train must have traveled four hours after the breakdown, at thirty mph. That 120, plus the sixty traveled before the breakdown, puts the stations 180 miles apart.

12. About eight, since the volume of a sphere increases with the cube of the radius.

13. The four parts should be 64, 20, 12, and 4.

14. Better stick with the dimes if you have a choice, but don't pass up a barrel full of silver dollars.

15. Just to show that I can do it, here's one solution:

     $123-4-5-6-7+8-9=100$ or $123-45-67+89=100$.

But there are lots of other solutions, of which, I'm sure, you have found several.

16. Pa is forty and I'm ten . . . but gaining on him.

17. Five airmails and twelve five-centers will do nicely.

18. The customer received eleven stamps and seven postcards, which he used in a big hurry before prices went up again.

19. Move the 7, 1 and 10, like this:

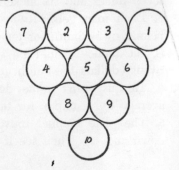

20. Make a nice triangular array, with four coins on each side.

21. Here's one way to do it: jump the 6 to the 9, the 4 to the 1, the 8 to the 3, the 10 to the 5, and the 2 to the 7—but there are other winning combinations.

22. Each hen must lay an egg every third day, so three hundred hens would lay thirty thousand eggs in three hundred days. Hope you like eggs.

23. Why, three, of course.

24. A picture is worth at least 250 words.

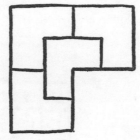

25. Not much I can say about this one. Hope you had fun with it.

26. Each boy received (and probably ate) two and two-thirds candy bars. Kevin contributed one-third of a bar to Brian, and David contributed two and one-third, so Kevin received two cents and David fourteen cents.

27. Thirty-two inches long, which is quite a fish story.

28. $49\overline{)1813}=37$.

From long ago and far away

1. Gauss paired off the smallest number, 1, with the largest, 100, 2 with 99, 3 with 98, and so on. He noted that each pair totaled 101, and that there were 50 pairs. The total of the number should be 50×101, or 5050.

2. Heck, with all those ninety-six solutions available, I hardly need take the space to tell you one or two.

3. Here is one solution. Rotate the board 90°, 180°, and 270° and you have three other solutions. Look at this solution from the back of the page, and you have another solution. Positions of the queens on the rows give a solution to the last puzzle.

Here are those magic squares:

4.

8	1	6
3	5	7
4	9	2

5.

23	9	19
13	17	21
15	25	11

6.

9	22	5
8	12	16
19	2	15

7.

10	3	8
5	7	9
6	11	4

8.

4	6	6	3
4	4	5	6
5	5	5	4
6	4	3	6

9. 1729.

10. The lady must be sixty-six.

11. Fibonacci concluded that the pairs of rabbits at the beginnings of the months would be 1, 1, 2, 3, 5, 8, 13, 21, 34, 55, 89, 144, and, at the beginning of the thirteenth month 233 pairs. But you may want to argue with his conclusion. In any event these numbers make up the Fibonacci sequence.

12. "Always" is a strong word, but this looks like a good bet.

13. The sum, each time, will be just one less than the second Fibonacci number after the last you added.

14. The black snake finally disappears after three and one-fifth days.

15. ∩∪O∪
        tasty coconuts.

16. Reckon 'bout eight thousand.

17. Here are a couple of solutions. There are others.

18. Try a star shape, or regular pentagram. Sarge would never believe it.

19. Eighty-four. You get a clue from its being the smallest number all those denominators will divide into evenly.

20. Eighty-eight and twelve.

21. Subtract 4 from both 100 and 20.

22. 36 is both a triangular and square number.

23. If you assumed that there was no paving under the large cube, each (large cube and plaza) would contain 512 little cubes. If you figure on paving under the large cube (and Plato didn't say), there must be 729 little cubes in each.

24. 28=14+7+4+2+1.

Build your own

1. If you experimented with two, three, and four disks, you must have discovered the pattern for the moves. With five disks you need thirty-one moves; with six, sixty-three; with sixty-four disks the priests needed $2^{64}-1$ moves, if they make no mistakes. And, apparently, they are at it yet!

2. I defer to the illustrator, but you should be able to build a more symmetrical answer.

3. Again:

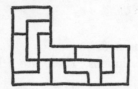

4. This problem is complicated a bit by the fact that, when you cut up a regular tetrahedron in the prescribed manner, you get some eight-faced figures (octahedra) in addition to the tetrahedra. I saw a fifth-grader solve this problem once by building a lot of tetrahedra and octahedra and fitting them together. I'll give you a plan for an octahedron if you want to try the same approach.

5. Eight little cubes will have three painted faces; twelve will have two; eight, three; and one will have no painted face.

6. 8/3; 24/2; 24/1; and 8/0.

7. There are thirty ways to paint a cube—but don't take my word for it. Make a bunch of little cubes and try your hand as an exterior decorator.

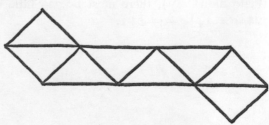

8. These are optical illusions.

9. There are many solutions for the first puzzle, including:

271		432	For the second	29786
271	and	432	I have	850
542		864		850
				31486

10. Did you fool your friend?

11. How did you do?

12. Now, you aren't really going to admit that problems a couple of seventh-graders made up have you stumped, are you?

13. As you must have found out, there is only one way to solve this problem. Make a mistake, and you have to begin again. With five pegs of each color, you need thirty-five moves to complete the switch.

14. How did it come out?

15. The magic number is 1089.

16.–18. Better check your plans!

19.–22. Find any takers on those bets?

Puzzles and patterns

1. $888 + 88 + 8 + 8 + 8$; $777/.7 - 77/.7$; $999 + 999/999$; $666/.666$; $(5+5)^{(5..5+.5)}$.

2. Probably just a bit more than twelve and four-sevenths seconds. Since there are seven pauses in the striking of eight, each pause must average about one and one-seventh seconds.

3. The circumference is increased by a yard, so the diameter will be increased by about a foot. Figure half on each side of the earth, and the rope stands about six inches above the earth.

4. If your weighing is strictly a matter of balancing weights against what you are weighing, then your best selection includes weights of one, two, four, eight, and sixteen grams. If you can place weights on the same side of the balance as the object being weighed, you can extend your range by using weights of one, three, nine, twenty-seven, and eighty-one grams.

5. The cork costs two and a half cents. Surely you didn't say five cents, did you?

6. My pinwheel is shown here:

7. The boys found $3.20.

8. John takes five minutes to run the mile. With a one-fifth-mile head start, he takes only four minutes for the four-fifths of a mile.

9. The fraction is one-seventh. .142857 is the decimal expansion . . . and you take it from there.

10. I'll tell you one of them: $1089 \times 9 = 9801$, but why don't you give the other part a bit more thought.

11. 'Twas a polar bear, no less, for he must have started at the North Pole.

12. $23 \times 47 = 1081$.

13. You could balance that little can with three balls.

14. Separate the eight coins into groups of three, three, and two. Put the groups of three on the balance. If they balance, the light coin is one of the other two, and you can catch it in one more weighing. If the groups of three do not balance, you'll know which has the light one. Take any two of that group and place one on each pan, and you will know which of the three is the phony.

15. The boys figured their average wrong. The one lad was actually selling tomatoes at six and two-thirds cents a piece the first day. The second, for seven and one-half cents. The average of these two figures is seven and one-twelfth cents. Sold at this price, the 120 tomatoes would have netted them $8.50.

16.

8	×	7	−	12	=	44
×		−		+		+
4	+	3	×	4	=	28
−		÷		−		÷
7		5		6		12
=		=		=		=
25	−	9	−	10	=	6

17.

3	×	4	+	7	=	19
+		+		×		×
7	−	5	÷	2	=	1
÷		−		−		÷
5	×	2	−	9	=	1
=		=		=		=
2	×	7	+	5	=	19

(There should be many solutions to this one.)

18. Arithmetic should be all like this!

19. Harry is now thirty-three and one-third years old, while Joe, at the sound of the tone, is forty-four and four-ninths years old . . . a rather unlikely age, I agree.

20. The number is 20.

21. Another pattern. Begin with an "all ones" number and work backward.

22. Break this down by half years, and you'll see that it's to your advantage to take the raise of $100 each half year. You will be ahead $100 each year (before taxes, of course).

23.

1	2	3	4
4	3	2	1
2	1	4	3
3	4	1	2

24.

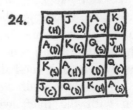

25.

4	1	3	5	2
3	5	2	4	1
2	4	1	3	5
1	3	5	2	4
5	2	4	1	3

26. P is twenty; q is five.

27. To trace this figure, start at one of the corners of the center square which is also an end of the diagonal. These points have an odd number of lines coming from them, and, since there are only two such, you can traverse the entire network.

28. 301 and 721.

29. Twenty girls and ten boys.

30. Now, if you heeded my advice on the other problem like this, you'll have no trouble at all with this one.

31. No one said the cuts had to be straight.

32. NINE

More puzzles

1. John is twenty-four; Mary is eighteen.

2. You may not like this, but pile the pennies in three piles of two each. Now arrange the three piles in a triangle. Sorry, but go try it on someone else.

3. When the thief takes nine steps, the officer's five are really equal to twelve and one-half thief steps, so the officer has gained three and one-half steps. Eight such gains will bring him even with the thief, which means the thief has taken 8×9=72 steps.

4. If he started just far enough north of the South Pole, so that when he had walked the ten miles due south he could walk a ten-mile circle "around the earth." Then ten miles north and he's home . . . but he'll see no bears.

5. 4 T 5=19; 3 T 9=30.

6. The trains will collide just one-half hour after the bee starts flying, so he must fly thirty miles.

7. Ninety-one feet, of course. You didn't say ninety-eight, by chance, did you?

8. 10^{12}, or an even trillion.

9. How about 12×13?

10. 321×112 will do nicely.

11. Since 35 percent of the book value is \$105, the whazzit must be worth about \$300.

12. The one train was going twice as fast as the other. If you aren't convinced, pick a couple of speeds and test my solution.

13. $3 \times \frac{3}{2} = 3 + \frac{3}{2}$. Now, what number can you add to 4 to get the same answer as when you multiply that number by 4?

14. Eight tens, twenty-four fives, and forty ones.

15. 59 minutes. Don't believe it? Catch a Glob and try this experiment.

16. The teller could handle the request with a fifty, a five, and four twos.

17. Suppose Jenny's glass would hold one cup of milk and Jeff's two cups. Then Jenny's glass had in it one-third cup of syrup, and Jeff's one-half cup of syrup. This makes five-sixths of a cup of syrup in a mixture of three cups, or five-eighteenths of the mixture.

18. Mother.

19. Look again at the dimensions of the field. The area is zero!

20. Nineteen nickels and sixteen dimes. Hurray for the Hungry Dog!

21. Amy could do half the job in one hour, and Wendy could do one-third the job in one hour. That means they have one-sixth left to do . . . which would take them another one-fifth of an hour.

22. Two miles is one-sixth of the distance, which must be twelve miles.

23. Here's a solution, but it leaves the coins not evenly spaced. Can you improve on this method? (The A's are pennies, B's are dimes, or vice versa.)

```
        A B A B A B A B
      A B       A B A B A B
      A B B A A       B A B
      A B B A A A B B
      A       A A A B B B B
```

24. 196.

25. A triangular arrangement.

26. Three and one-thirteenth cords, but I'll bet they quit with an even three.

27. There are twenty-eight dominoes in the "up to double six" set, and there must be about forty-five in the double nine set.

28. $\lvert\lvert = \lvert\lvert\lvert\lvert - \lvert\lvert$

29. Place that top penny on top of the corner penny and you'll have it.

30. Since it must take one and one-third minutes per cut, you'll take five and one-third minutes for the four cuts on the five-foot piece.

CHARLES F. LINN, the author of PUZZLES, PATTERNS, AND PASTIMES, was born in Pennsylvania. A graduate of Colgate, he later went to Wesleyan University in Connecticut, where he earned a Masters degree and, along the way, gained, as he says, "my first insights into what math is all about, and the idea that everyone can be creative in math at his own level."

Mr. Linn then taught mathematics in public schools, and later was the mathematics editor and writer for two nationally circulated classroom science newspapers. He is currently teaching at Oswego State College in upper New York State, and owns a 200 year old summer house on Turkey Hill Road in Haddam, Connecticut. It is at this retreat that he has written his previous books—a mathematics textbook, several mathematics pamphlets, and a four volume history of mathematics series. In spite of his full work load, he still finds time every year for the celebration of Susan B. Anthony's birthday, and the commemoration of the crossing of the River Boyne by King William.

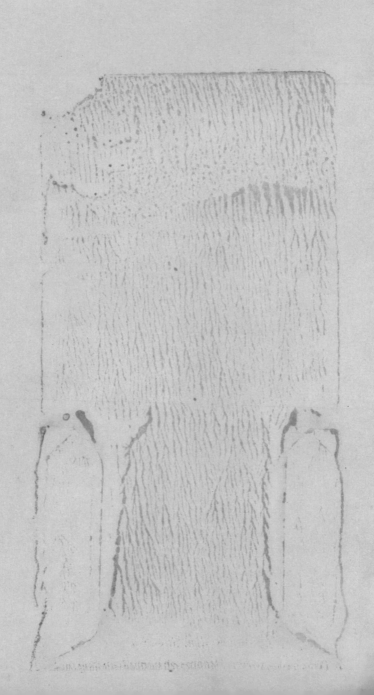